GW00391771

Letters from transplant recipients to donors' families

thank you
for life

**Royal College
of Physicians**

The Royal College of Physicians

The Royal College of Physicians (RCP) is a registered charity that aims to ensure high quality care for patients by promoting the highest standards of medical practice. It provides and sets standards in clinical practice and education and training, conducts assessments and examinations, quality assures external audit programmes, supports doctors in their practice of medicine, and advises the government, public and the profession on healthcare issues.

Department of Health

The Department of Health exists to improve the health and wellbeing of people in England.

NHS Blood and Transplant

NHS Blood and Transplant (NHSBT) is the UK organ donation and transplantation organisation. A special health authority, NHSBT is responsible for all aspects of the donation process and for matching and allocating organs for transplantation, as well as campaigning to raise awareness of donation. Its remit also includes the provision of a reliable, efficient supply of blood and associated services to the NHS.

Copyright © Royal College of Physicians 2010

All rights reserved. No part of this publication may be reproduced in any form (including photocopying or storing it in any medium by electronic means and whether or not transiently or incidentally to some other use of this publication) without the written permission of the copyright owner. Applications for the copyright owner's written permission to reproduce any part of this publication should be addressed to the publisher.

The RCP has made every effort to collect and present the most accurate information in this book and the information published here was believed to be correct at the time of publication.

ISBN: 978-1-86016-407-1

Royal College of Physicians
11 St Andrews Place, Regent's Park, London NW1 4LE. www.rcplondon.ac.uk

Registered Charity No 210508

Designed, typeset and edited by the Publications Department at the Royal College of Physicians. Printed in Great Britain by Charlesworth Press, Wakefield, West Yorkshire.

Foreword Sir Roy Calne iv
Preface Professor Andrew Burroughs
& Linda Selves v
Introduction Donor family representatives viii

Helen transplant recipient 2–3
Joan transplant recipient 4
Michael transplant recipient 5
Anonymous transplant recipient 5
T McE transplant recipient 6
Stan transplant recipient 7
Anonymous husband of transplant recipient 7
Aislinn transplant recipient 8–9
Maureen mother of transplant recipient 10
Jackie transplant recipient 11
Diane transplant recipient 12–13
Philip transplant recipient 14
Anonymous wife of transplant recipient 15

The Transplant Games 2010 16–19

Anonymous transplant recipient 20
Deborah transplant recipient 20
Brian transplant recipient 21
Susan transplant recipient 22–25

Shirley transplant recipient 26
Paul transplant recipient 26–27
Diana transplant recipient 28–31
Anonymous transplant recipient 32
Brenda wife of transplant recipient 32
Patricia transplant recipient 33
Kay transplant recipient 33
Pamela transplant recipient 34–35
Nora transplant recipient 36
Alberto transplant recipient 37
Anonymous transplant recipient 37
Steve transplant recipient 38–41
Anonymous transplant recipient & recipient's family 42–43
Theresa transplant recipient 43
Sophie transplant recipient & recipient's family 44–45
Trevor transplant recipient 45
Michael transplant recipient 46
John transplant recipient & recipient's family 47
Mahendra & Sunita transplant recipient & recipient's wife 48–51

Mandip son, brother & organ donor 52–53
Lloyd brother of organ donor 54

Further information 55
Acknowledgements 56

"... There is a shortage of donors worldwide, but education and government action can lead to remarkable generosity on the part of the public..."

Organ transplantation has been an extraordinary success story, blossoming remarkably quickly after the first kidney transplant between identical twins in 1954. Efforts to overcome rejection of transplants between individuals who are not genetically identical, together with significant improvements in surgical techniques and medical management, have now delivered a new treatment that can bring life to people otherwise doomed. Not surprisingly, there has been an increasing demand for grafts of all transplanted vital organs. This success has led to an increase in the greatest problem, namely the shortage of organ donors. Kidney transplants can be donated by live donors – usually family members – and the same is true to a lesser extent with the liver. However, the major sources of organ donation worldwide are deceased donors, usually victims of accidents or brain haemorrhage.

There is a shortage of donors worldwide, but education and government action can lead to remarkable generosity on the part of the public; this has been the case particularly in some European countries. In the UK, the donations from deceased donors have not increased as much, and it is hoped that this book, *Thank you for life*, will help to activate the natural charitable instincts of most people. The letters published are extraordinarily poignant. No matter how expressed, the feelings of gratitude to the donor and sympathy to the relatives are a tribute to their generosity and a testament to the joy of the contributors at being restored to a normal life for many years.

Sir Roy Calne FRS
Emeritus professor of surgery, University of Cambridge
Visiting professor, National University of Singapore

"Compiling this book has been in our thoughts for the past three years. We have both been professionally involved with liver transplantation for over 20 years, and continue to marvel at the 'Lazarus' effect of this treatment. Patients suffering during the end stage of cirrhosis, with only a few months to live, often after years of unemployment due to their illness, usually hospital bound, and with difficult family lives, are transformed. A few months after surgery, they are fully restored to their spouses, partners, children, extended family and friends. They can have children if they wish, and are able to work; many do both. Other patients with acute liver failure, previously in normal health, can become seriously ill within days, facing certain death, but return rapidly to a full life thanks to a liver transplant.

Although the success of organ transplantation of all types depends on the integration of many specialist teams before, during and after the procedure, nothing would be possible without the individuals and their families who agree to donate organs: the donors.

Our involvement with patients who undergo transplantation also led us to wonder why donors are not remembered, indeed celebrated, much more by society and by the health profession. We believe that the letters in this book, written by patients who have had transplants, to their anonymous organ donors and the donors' families, epitomise and symbolise what transplantation is all about. The letters are real life stories, which express not only thanks (which in spirit is never-ending), but also document the remarkable legacies of the courageous, selfless and generous gift of donation.

Organ donation is the giving of a gift, and should remain so. Although the gift is passed from one individual to another, many more people experience the benefits. It is not a resource, and indeed, no amount of money can buy it. Being a gift, it should be celebrated and acknowledged by society as a whole. These letters, we know, have been appreciated by the families and friends of each donor involved, and both they and the recipients have given permission to publish them.

Bethany, transplant recipient, and her father Andy at the Transplant Games (see p16–19)

"...I WISH I'D WRITTEN A LETTER TO THE DONOR FAMILY. I COULDN'T FIND THE WORDS. EVERY SECOND THAT IT HAS GIVEN US IS A BONUS. I'D LIKE TO WRITE TO THEM NOW AND TRY TO EXPLAIN, BUT I'M WORRIED I'VE LEFT IT TOO LATE..."

ANDY – FATHER OF TRANSPLANT RECIPIENT

However, we wish this book to be much more; that is, to represent a medium through which all donors and their families, past, present and future, are publicly thanked and celebrated, especially those families who themselves have never received a letter.

This book is published, launched, and presented under the auspices of the Royal College of Physicians (RCP), and forms part of its continued commitment to organ donation. It is also a formal recognition and thanks from the RCP on behalf of the health profession, to donors and their families.

We encourage everyone reading these letters – or listening to them being read in the classroom, or in public, or on the radio or on stage – to think about how much good can be done, without need of any money, by donating their organs for others.

The challenge of donation is to think about it in the present, for the future, so as to make it easier to discuss this special gift within families, or with friends. This will ensure that relatives and friends are in no doubt as to what one's wishes are when they die. The challenge to oneself is 'dare to give'. We believe that this will be made easier by this book, and by society regularly celebrating and recognising donors and their families, as they give life to others across generations, who in turn benefit their communities and society as a whole.

We hope that this book, which contains neither statistics nor targets, but just heartfelt letters from those receiving organs to their donor, will leave a mark in each heart and be a constant encouragement to make the personal decision to give.

Professor Andrew Burroughs FRCP FMedSci
Consultant physician, Royal Free Hospital
Professor of hepatology, University College London

Linda Selves MSc RN
Senior liver transplant coordinator, Royal Free Hospital

"... This book is for those families who have said 'yes' and for their family member who is missed so much..."

As families who have lost someone dear to us in sudden and tragic circumstances, it has been really important to know that something good has come out of such despair. For some of us, making the decision to allow our loved one's organs to be used for transplantation was made easier by knowing what their wishes would have been. For others, however, it was difficult, and involved wrestling with the natural desire to protect them from any further intervention, against the knowledge that someone else might live if we could be brave enough. We have not regretted our decision. Hearing the impact of donation through the letters in this book, and the letters we have received personally from the families helped by our relative's precious gift, gives us and many other donor families pride and comfort that so much has been achieved.

These letters were written for specific families, but their meaning and impact extends to all families whose loved one's achievement has given hope and transformation to the lives of others.

This book is for those families who have said "yes" and for their family member who is missed so much.

Signed by donor family representatives

Betty Burgess   *Colin Burgess*

*Harvey, transplant recipient,
and his mother at the Transplant
Games (see p16–19)*

"...this ability to delight in the mundane and to live in the 'Now' becomes more and more central and with it comes a deep appreciation for the simplest pleasures in life..."

Dear Sir/Madam

I had a liver transplant on 15.07.96 two days after my baby daughter was born. I feel very guilty that I have taken so long to write and thank the donor's family, but it has not been an easy letter to write. Now, however, I hope that around the anniversary of her death my letter will go some way towards alleviating the enormous grief they must feel. Without the transplant I would certainly have died leaving my husband to look after our newborn baby on his own. Like most transplant patients the gift of life has been amazing and words can never express just how grateful we really are.

I have signed off the letter Helen and enclosed a picture of Ella, our baby; should you choose to respond I trust the Royal Free will forward me any letter.

Yours sincerely, Helen

Ella is now 14 years of age and has had the love and support of her mother throughout her life, which has been a priceless gift to her.

Dear Family

After a long silence – it's been ten years since my last letter – it's a relief to be writing again and sharing some good news with you, as well as feeling able to reiterate my deepest heartfelt thanks to you all for the amazing gift of life that your grandmother/mother gave me, my friends and my family, by donating her liver to save my life.

I have so much to be grateful for and to celebrate that is marvellous and I am pleased to say that one of the legacies of being a transplant patient is that I really appreciate the small things in life, as much as the more sublime. Being fit and healthy and being able to spend time with family and friends is so important to me, as is doing the most ordinary things with them. My daughter Ella is now a beautiful teenager and every year on her birthday I am reminded how blessed we are because that is the time of my transplant. I have lots of photographs of her and I thought I would share a handful of them with you to convey just how grateful we are that she's had her Mum and her Dad to lean on over the last 14 years.

Talking to people who have experienced amazing recoveries or near misses, I am struck by how similar their responses are. There seems to be a common theme running through their stories. This ability to delight in the mundane and to live in the "Now" becomes more and more central and with it comes a deep appreciation for the simplest pleasures in life, like walking the dog, watching our children smile and tease us, sharing a spontaneous picnic in an unlikely place or chatting to a stranger with a sense of humour.

Gift of Life,
oil on canvas,
Helen Eccles
(cover illustration).

My husband William lost his first wife through breast cancer and so we feel doubly blessed to have found each other and to have built a new life together. We have been married for six years and I'm delighted to say that our marriage just gets better and better.

There are five doctors in my family and I have always wanted to be one too. For ages I wondered how I could ever repay the hospital, the doctors and the nurses for all they did for me. Together we won several big battles against the most extraordinary odds in Intensive Care. Recently I've realised that the answer lay in finding out what I was really good at and seem born to do. I searched and searched and of course the answer was right here in front of me all along. I like helping others find their true calling and work out what it is that gives them meaning in their lives and a deep connection with their intuitive wisdom. I have set myself up as a "coach" and I find it deeply rewarding work.

John D Russell said, "I never cease to be amazed at the power of the coaching process to draw out the skills or talent that was previously hidden within an individual, and which invariably finds a way to solve a problem previously thought unsolvable." I think that's what we all did in the Royal Free after Ella was born and why each of us succeeded so brilliantly. We coached each other through the bleak and difficult bits and also dropped the doctor patient divide and replaced it with something much more powerful and profoundly human. Thank you again for making that miracle possible.

Best wishes, Helen

The picture I painted is an abstract version of Duccio's scenes in the Maesta, which hangs in the National Gallery. I love the colours of his Annunciation, when the angel swoops down to bless Mary with a child. I therefore spent time sketching the colours from the original before producing my own transcription.

"...Transplantation is much more than a physical miracle. It is a bonding of humanity, and has altered and enhanced my life in so many ways; I cannot adequately express my gratitude..."

I have known for some time that it was your daughter who gave me back my life and my health. When I first heard of your enquiry I was not sure it was me as there was another woman, only a little bit younger than me, who had her liver transplant a few days after me, at the same hospital, and it was some months before I knew for certain. When I did know, much as I wanted to write, I found it very difficult.

I think you know that I am in my sixties. It must have been a disappointment to you that it was not a younger person's life that was saved. And I was shocked to know that such a young life had contributed to mine. I can only say that I treasure the thought of her life, and feel so privileged.

I want you to know that my new lease of life has enabled my six grandchildren to have an active and loving grandmother, and I seem to be very important to each of them. The two youngest are Indian, and live in India, and I am their link with the British roots and this side of the family. I have also been able to make good use of the experience of my working life, and work actively with teachers, and as a school governor, with more energy than I have had for many years.

I want to tell you that when I had my transplant there was a very strong feeling of what I can only describe as love amongst us all, and I felt proud and at the same time humbled to be part of the whole team, of all those involved. At first I would have found it very difficult to be told anything about my donor, to have to dwell on the tragedy that enabled me to live, and on your bereavement, and I thought of my new life as a gift from humanity – and of course it is that. But shortly before I first heard that you wanted to hear from me I had been asking my consultant if there was anything I could be told.

One further thing I would like to say; two days before my transplant I was told there was a donor liver for me, but then the relative decided against it. That made me all the more aware of your own generous decision.

I am very glad that you asked to hear from me, and very sorry that it has taken me so long to be able to write to you. It is strange to think that I do not know you, that I do not know anything about you at all, not even whether you have other children. But, I think of you.

Transplantation is much more than a physical miracle. It is a bonding of humanity, and has altered and enhanced my life in so many ways; I cannot adequately express my gratitude.

Joan's letter was the inspiration for this book, read out at her memorial service by her grandchildren, almost 20 years after her liver transplant.

Dear Friend

I am writing after what must seem a long time to express my gratitude to your relative, and also to you, for making my liver transplant possible by allowing the selfless donation by your loved one to go ahead.

It must have been a very difficult decision to have made in what must have been a very sad time for you all. I hope it may help to know that this act saved my life, for which I will be eternally grateful.

As I say, you will have to forgive me for not thanking you sooner, but after a successful transplant I unfortunately developed other complications prolonging my stay in hospital by another six months. Thankfully I am now at home and getting stronger by the day.

Your loved one will always be remembered in my prayers, and I promise to light a candle to her memory on each anniversary of her death and of my transplant.

Once again I cannot thank you enough for saving my life.

Sorry for the handwriting, Michael

"...I just want to thank you from the bottom of my heart, for giving me this gift ... you are in my thoughts and prayers every day..."

Dear Friends

I am writing this letter to give my thanks to you. I am a woman, 53 years of age; I have 4 children, 3 daughters, 1 son and a granddaughter. During August of last year I had a liver transplant. I had been very ill for some years and also had a rare lung disorder with which I had to be on oxygen constantly. I was suffering a lot of pain every day for some time. By the end of 2001 I was admitted to hospital as I was deteriorating. So with the transplant I have had my life saved. Also the transplant cured my lung disorder.

I remained in hospital for 4 months after the operation as I was still on very high oxygen. I have been writing letter after letter to you, but I cannot seem to get it right. It is so hard to put into words how grateful I, and my family are to your loved one and you for showing such kindness and generosity, at what was such a tragic and awful time for you. I have so much

admiration for your bravery. I am almost back to normal now, every day is such a joy and a bonus and I get so much out of life now. It is just so wonderful to not have pain every day.

I just want to thank you from the bottom of my heart, for giving me this gift. You are in my thoughts and prayers every day. God bless to your loved one and you.

With greatest love and thanks to you.

This lady had her liver transplant 9 years ago. She had a prolonged recovery but within a couple of years was taking part in the National Transplant Games (see p16–19). She is the central figure of her family and supports them all.

generous

"...my heart was with you and is still with you. Your loved one is with me, literally, with every breath I take. I promise to honour you both with everything I do..."

Dear Family

On January 19th 2008 I received a liver from your loved one.

I have been meaning to write this letter from the moment I was called for my operation, knowing then that I may not even be the most suitable recipient for that liver, but as it happened, I was. I suppose this letter may be difficult to read. It has been difficult to write. It is both painful and joyous. The reason I am writing is to thank you.

"Thank you" is an expression which is used quite often and sometimes just in passing. This is not that kind of "Thank you". It is a different "Thank you", one that defies English, or for that matter, any language on earth. But how does one say thank you to someone who because of you and your loved one's generosity I am alive today and continue living. This is not simply a gift of an organ; it is a gift of life. I don't know how one can truly express one's feelings in words for giving someone a life.

I can however but try. I must try, because I think you should know that this life that was saved, is a life of promise. Words are not adequate but that's all I can use to attempt to express my gratitude to you and your loved one; part of whom gave me life.

How do I share with you that you have given me back my life? In fact what you gave me is a better life. My wife and family also thank you.

I think you should know that not one day goes by that I do not think of the generous spirit of yours and the man who enabled me to be healthy again. I had mixed emotions during that ride to hospital. Not because I was scared or happy but because I knew that on that day, somewhere, a family lost a precious, beloved person in their life.

My heart was with you and is still with you. Your loved one is with me, literally, with every breath I take. I promise to honour you both with everything I do, especially for others who have suffered like me.

If you have any special requests at all, just let me know. With all my heart, I wish you peace. I wish you love. Thank you.

With all the love from the deepest part of my love, T McE

Dear Friends

I was sorry to hear about the loss of one of your family, so I hope the next few words I write will help you in your grief.

Please let me explain. For a very long time I have had a liver disease and I am the one who received the member of your family's liver, for which it will give me a second chance at life, and I shall be forever grateful.

God bless you, Stan

Stan had a new lease of life following his liver transplant 8 years ago and fulfilled a long ambition to visit friends in Australia.

Dear Friends

We cannot express enough words of appreciation for the donation of your child's liver. We understand how it must feel to lose a child and the grief that you are suffering. We would like to tell you that grief has come to some good in that through your kindness my wife has a new lease of life.

We will take good care of this liver. We would like to plant a tree in the memory of your daughter at a place which is special.

The recipient did indeed plant a tree in memory of her young donor at Wimpole Hall, near Cambridge, and has continued to take good care of her liver for the past 10 years.

"...We would like to tell you that grief has come to some good in that through your kindness my wife has a new lease of life..."

"...I wake every day and thank my donor for the gift of life. It takes a very special person to be so giving and to think of others at such a critical time..."

Dear Family

My name is Aislinn and I am 31 years old. I find that writing this letter is both joyful and difficult.

Difficult, as I know this letter will remind you of a very sad and difficult time in your lives and of someone you loved a great deal.

I have wanted to write for a long time, but I also wanted to give you some space and time to grieve for your loss. I hope that my writing does not offend you or seem inappropriate.

The gift of a liver has been one of the most joyous days of my life. I had been ill most of my life and seriously ill the few months leading up to April '08. I suffer from a progressive autoimmune liver disease called Primary Sclerosing Cholangitis. If it had not been for your donation I would have died. I cannot thank you enough and it seems to me there are no words that I can think of to express the feelings I have inside. I just hope that you will feel up to getting in touch with me through the coordinators. I would very much love to hear from all or any of you.

My health is fantastic, just trying to get fit and eat healthily like any normal person. I wake every day and thank my donor for the gift of life. It takes a very special person to be so giving and to think of others at such a critical time.

I just hope that I can live up to expectations and am trying my hardest to do so. Hoping to hear from you soon.

Your friend

Aislinn married shortly before her liver transplant and has had the last 2 years to really enjoy her new status with good health.

Dear Cathy, Peter, Luke and Simon

Simon, Tansy and I wish you a peaceful New Year. Thank you for Emma's photograph. She was beautiful. I have not shown the photograph to Simon. I do not think that he could bear to see it. He is so conscious that she has enabled him to live.

When Simon was in ITU after his transplant, Tansy used to talk to Emma's liver. She welcomed it, said it was now safe after its trauma and told it about Simon. That he was gentle and would look after it.

Simon is indeed well. He works part time, not because of his health, but because there is not a large market for artists. Last year he worked with a local youth club. He teaches desk top publishing to enable them to produce a magazine, which circulates local schools and youth clubs. They call him Simon-Flymo.

Also he is doing a digital arts project in the Lea Valley park and helped young volunteers to produce a video for the youth offending team. It is a very graphic account of the effects of stealing from shops – including interviews from shop keepers who have been attacked/robbed. The authority say that it is better than their commercially produced video and are going to circulate it to schools and market it.

This year he has been commissioned to produce another video for the team and to facilitate a mural at a local primary school. He does this by holding workshops with the children, where they draw their ideas. These he scans into his computer, to produce a number of mural designs. The children choose which one they want and he draws it onto the wall. The children then paint it.

I spent yesterday with Simon and Tansy in their new home. They cooked a chestnut pie, with chestnuts gathered from the park and vegetables grown in their allotment. After that we had home made chocolate, which they were experimenting with and played anti-monopoly. It was a lovely day for which we are all grateful to you.

I hope that the recent fires around Sydney have not affected you. There has been a lot of coverage on them over here on TV.

With best wishes, Maureen

Simon had his first transplant in 1994 for acute liver failure. The liver saved Simon's life but sadly two months later, the artery connecting the liver became blocked and Simon had to be listed for a second transplant. Eight years following his second transplant, Simon developed problems that could only be treated by another liver transplant.

He approached this with his usual quiet courage and throughout supported his mother and fiancée. Following that transplant, Simon and Tansy married and he continues to appreciate good heath and happiness, nine years on.

Cathy, Emma's mother wished to add her comments regarding the letters that she receives from Maureen.

"My letters from Maureen over the years have been a source of great comfort and inspiration and the fact Simon continues to do so well gives our family great pride in Emma's wishes to be a donor.

Also, I think it is very important to note that the donors with the consent of their families are always considered 'special' but it takes a huge degree of courage for the recipient and/ or their family to actually take the step to say 'thank you' in some form but the effect it has on the donor's family is immeasurable in so many ways."

Dear Friends

This is the most difficult letter I have ever had to write so please forgive my shaking writing.

There are no words to express the heartfelt gratitude both I, and my family feel for the very precious gift you have given me, which I promise to take great care of now and always.

I know only too well that no words of sorrow, sympathy or comfort can go any way to heal your loss – only time can do that, but it may help just a little to know what your precious gift has done, not only for me, but my family also so I thought I would tell you a little about myself:

I am just an ordinary mum of 42 years, who lives for her family, but through no fault of my own has suffered with the liver disease known as primary biliary cirrhosis, for the last 10 years, until it got to the stage where my only hope was a transplant. My family are my two lovely children, mum and dad, who have always been there for me, and now with my transplant I will hopefully be able to lead a more normal life

than I have been these last few years – and help my children achieve their goals.

My beautiful, clever daughter is 15 years old and wants to train to be a veterinary nurse, and my son will be 18 years old in September – I was not sure I would be able to celebrate his special day as I became more and more ill.

My family and I thank you from the bottom of our hearts and I promise you that not a day goes by without me thinking of you all. If you would like to know anything else or would like to know in the future of my progress I would be only to happy and willing and will let my transplant coordinator know.

In the meantime God bless you all – you will always be in our thoughts.

Jackie

"...MY FAMILY AND I THANK YOU FROM THE BOTTOM OF OUR HEARTS AND I PROMISE YOU THAT NOT A DAY GOES BY WITHOUT ME THINKING OF YOU ALL...."

"...I would love you to know that my family will now have a wife and mother who they would have lost, due solely to your bravery and compassion in making the decision you did, enabling me to live..."

Dear Family

Would you please allow me to offer you my deepest sympathy on the loss of your daughter and sister.

I am writing to you as a very overwhelmed and grateful recipient of a new liver, which will give me the chance of new life I would not otherwise have expected to have. For this great privilege I have only you and your recently lost daughter and sister to be everlastingly thankful to.

I am a woman of 53 years with a wonderful husband and 2 marvellous daughters of 25 and 26 years, so imagine I can appreciate, in a very small way, your great loss. Nothing can replace her; but I would love you to know that my family will now have a wife and mother who they would have lost, due solely to your bravery and compassion in making the decision you did, enabling me to live.

I will forever respect and appreciate the great gift you have allowed me, and, although I am at a loss as to how to thank you enough for what you have done for me, I offer you my most heartfelt and sincerest thanks and gratitude for the rest of my life.

Yours sincerely, Diane

The 14 years following her liver transplant have seen Diane become a grandmother and she treasures her time with her family.

"...I AM VERY THANKFUL FOR THE SECOND CHANCE OF LIFE THAT I HAVE BEEN GIVEN. IN PARTICULAR I AM THANKFUL THAT DIANA AND I CAN CONTINUE BRINGING UP OUR CHILDREN TOGETHER..."

Dear Friends

Let me introduce myself first. My name is Philip, I am married to Diana and we have two young children, Jessica and Jonathan. I was the fortunate recipient of the liver of your relative who so sadly, and I suspect suddenly, died in June. I had been taken ill about three weeks earlier and within a week found myself in hospital. After just two weeks there I was told that my liver had deteriorated so rapidly and to such an extent that I needed a transplant urgently. The doctors never did discover the reason for my sudden and rather dramatic illness.

Literally hours after I was put on the urgent list I was told that a healthy liver of just the right size was available for me and the following morning I was in theatre having the transplant. The operation went well and so did my recovery: just four weeks after the operation I was allowed

home. I am still of course not at all strong, but I am gaining strength daily, if slowly: I am told it will take about four months before I am fully fit again.

After the initial shock of falling so ill (I am normally a healthy person) and being told I would need a transplant, I am very thankful for the second chance of life that I have been given. In particular I am very thankful that Diana and I can continue bringing up our children together. The experience has made me stop and think, and value life and health that before I took largely for granted.

However, I am also very aware that my life-saving operation has come at a huge cost to you and to your loved one, and that while we are feeling relief at the safe ending to an alarming episode in our lives you are mourning someone you loved very much.

I know the fact that her liver helped an unknown person many miles away cannot compensate for the huge personal loss and grief you must feel. All I can say is thank you so much for consenting to the donation of her liver: it must have been an awful decision to have to make at such a time, but it saved my life.

I do think of you and pray for you, even though I do not know you.

With all good wishes, Philip

Following acute liver failure, Philip made a good recovery and it is now 8 years since his transplant. He has been able to be there, as a father, for his two children, to give them love and guidance over the years.

Dear Friends

This is a letter to thank you for the gift of life my husband received, for which we will be forever grateful to you.

My husband is 50 years old. He is a rather humorous man, very kind and caring and always ready to help everybody. He is also a very loving husband and father. He has two daughters. He is clearly loved by us and our families and highly respected in his profession for his knowledge and integrity.

Until the end of last year he was a healthy, strong and energetic person full of life. Then he was prescribed some drugs for a suspected symptomless illness, which was never confirmed and suddenly his liver was destroyed by the drugs. Within 6 weeks he was at death's door, unconscious and oblivious of what was happening to him. We were practically destroyed with grief as were his parents and three siblings.

Then, at the last minute on the 13th of February he received a transplant. He had numerous complications and for over a month he remained in intensive care where he, doctors, nurses and coordinators battled to save him. Then he moved to the high dependency ward for nearly two months and was finally allowed home for his birthday in May.

He was very weak and just skin and bones, and could hardly walk then, but he was alive.

Now he has put on some weight, is walking by himself, is talking like himself, and he is looking forward to a complete recovery and a full life again. He is finding it difficult to come to terms with the whole tragedy, but he is strong and he will. He appreciates he has a new lease of life and he is very grateful and determined to honour it the best he can.

On his behalf, our daughters', our families and myself I thank you. My life would not be worth much without him.

I am very aware that you have suffered the distress of losing your loved one. I sincerely empathise with your sorrow. I hope that this letter will be of some comfort to you in the knowledge that some good has, nevertheless, come out of such terrible sadness.

I pray for her peace and for your happiness. With love

Five years after his liver transplant, this gentleman continues to enjoy good health and his family are relieved and overjoyed that he remains an important part of their lives.

> *"...he appreciates he has a new lease of life and he is very grateful and determined to honour it the best he can..."*

"...Before the transplant Ellis was so weak that he was in a wheelchair. He's now living a young boy's life and we're grateful for every day that we have..."

Trevor – father of transplant recipient

The Transplant Games Bath 2010

The impact of the decision to donate organs can clearly be seen at the annual British Transplant Games. The games provide a real opportunity to celebrate the new life that results from a transplant. A tribute is made at the opening ceremony to all donors and their families whose decision gave the participants the chance to be there and to live life again. Many children take part, accompanied by grateful parents, whose messages of thanks reinforce the sentiment of this book.

"WITHOUT THE BRAVE DECISION OF A DONOR FAMILY, MY SON WOULDN'T BE HERE TAKING PART IN THE GAMES AND SHARING HIS TRIUMPHS WITH HIS TWIN BROTHER" JAMES – FATHER

British Transplant Games
Bath 2010

103

Dear Friends

I am writing to say thank you for making my liver transplant possible. You will never know how sorry I am for your loss, but also how incredibly grateful I am for the gift of life that I have been given.

I was diagnosed with liver cancer over a year ago. My family and friends were devastated and I was in shock. After periods of chemotherapy and embolisation I was assessed and accepted onto the UK Transplant List/Register. This became a "beacon of hope" in a dark period of time.

Since the transplant I have had a new lease of life. I can now plan for the future and hope to enjoy many more years with precious friends, family, children and grandchildren.

As this card says…

Your gift has given me HOPE for a future with my family and friends. I now BELIEVE even more in the power of prayer and that "miracles" can happen! My DREAMS can now become a possibility – whereas before I could not even dare to dream!

Finally, your gift has given me "endless possibilities!"

THANK YOU! From a very grateful recipient

To a Special Mum

It feels good to be able to put pen to paper at last and to thank you from the bottom of my heart for the gift of life your daughter has given me and for the kindness and compassion you have shown.

I am so sorry that it has taken this long time before writing to you. I realise now that my decision not to write might have been wrong but at the time, I was afraid that you might have felt I was intruding in your life and I didn't want to add to your grief. I also realise that by not thanking you and your family, I was not expressing gratitude for my own life.

My name is Deborah and I am now 39 years old. I am engaged to Mark and we are planning to get married in May this year.

I want to say to you that it was a wonderful thing that you did as a mother that in your deep sadness showed a caring and giving heart.

I have a much better quality of life now since coming off dialysis 5 years ago. My father died of kidney failure when I was 3 years old. He was someone I would have loved to have known.

I often think about your daughter, who she was and what she was like. Despite not knowing her, I think about her with affection and much respect.

These last years must have been extremely painful for you all. I really hope that you, your family and friends have found peace in your lives.

Love, Deborah

Deborah had her transplant 12 years ago and remains well and grateful for this amazing gift.

"…I want to say to you that it was a wonderful thing that you did as a mother that in your deep sadness showed a caring and giving heart…"

Dear Friends

It is now three weeks since I received my life saving transplant and I am making good progress.

Ever since I regained consciousness I have been thinking of you and wanting to write to you.

I want to express my sincere and heartfelt sympathy for your tragic loss. I can imagine how painful this tragedy must be for you.

My family were trying to prepare themselves for my death, which would have happened within a very short time had it not been for the transplant. I have been chronically ill most of my life and would soon have died.

My wife and I have an 11 year old daughter. We can imagine how we would feel if she suddenly died. We know you are good and caring people and that your daughter was too. You must have known she would want to help others like me.

Thank you for bringing your daughter up to be so caring and considerate, and thank you for having the courage, in the face of overwhelming grief to carry out her wish to be an organ donor. I hope I can live the rest of my life in a way which is worthy of this tremendous gift.

Thank you

Brian has returned to his career in teaching, following his two liver transplants and enjoys being with his family.

"...thank you for having the courage, in the face of overwhelming grief to carry out her wish to be an organ donor..."

"...I BECAME SO ILL THAT I HARDLY LEFT MY ROOM FOR 18 MONTHS. I JUST WANTED TO BE WELL ENOUGH TO RAISE A HAPPY AND HEALTHY CHILD AND THAT'S WHAT THIS TRANSPLANT HAS MADE POSSIBLE..."

SUSAN - TRANSPLANT RECIPIENT

"...I CANNOT BEGIN TO TELL YOU WHAT YOUR TREMENDOUS GIFT MEANS TO ME AND MY FAMILY. I HAVE STRUGGLED TO FIND A WORD THAT IS SUFFICIENTLY APPRECIATIVE AND BIG ENOUGH TO SAY THANK YOU..."

Dear Friends

Please allow me to tell you a little bit about myself. I am a married woman with a little 5½ year old boy called Harry. My name is Susan and my husband is called Andrew. Harry is a charismatic and energetic bundle of fun and love.

I have lived with chronic liver disease since the age of 11. Six years ago my health took a turn for the worse. A year and a half ago I found myself becoming progressively house bound and in the end totally relying on others to care for both my family and myself, life at home was just horrendous.

I cannot begin to tell you what your tremendous gift means to me and my family. I have struggled to find a word that is sufficiently appreciative and big enough to say thank you.

A year and some months ago I took Harry, then 4 years old, to our very local play area. It was time for Harry to have his bicycle stabilisers removed; after two sessions, a box of plasters and an aching back on my part, Harry was just about able to cycle a distance of about 15 metres. Later on that week my health took a turn for the worse and steadily deteriorated to a point where I was housebound and then bed bound: no more visits to the play area with Harry, no more helping Harry to develop his bicycle skills, no more drop offs or pick ups from school. Instead, I watched from my bedroom window or from my bed and slowly, very slowly I watched a year in my son's life tick past. Family life was not good, my husband's work suffered, he became extremely tired and desperate as he took on more and more responsibilities in the home.

Your gift to me has meant so much and to give you a small example of just how much your gift has meant to us, please imagine this scenario.

Harry and I were at our local play area last week, his stabilisers were taken off again and I was able to help Harry to ride his bike without his stabilisers. It had been over a year since he had last attempted this, no plasters, no bad back on my part, instead we had smiles and tears of joy and the glow of confidence beaming from Harry, it took just 2 days to bring everything back to us, my husband joined us at the play area, and together we had a great and memorable family time together.

I can honestly say that the memory of the three of us just "being", smiling, holding each other and crying will live with me forever.

I do not know what normal is, but we do know we have found a new happiness and new warmth together as a family.

Thank you so much for your tremendous courage. We are well and truly back on track again, now I am able to hold my husband and son in a way that I have not been able to do for a very, very long time.

Thank you
Thank you so much
Susan, Andrew and Harry

It has now been over 5 years since Susan's transplant and Harry not needing stabilisers. Instead, Susan has the energy to cheer Harry on at all his sporting events and treasures each precious day.

My name is Shirley

I wish to take this opportunity to express my deepest sympathy for your sad loss and to thank you for his wonderful gift, which has given me the opportunity to have a better life. He must have been a wonderful person.

I am 59 years of age and have been in poor health for most of my adult life due to kidney disease. I was informed by the hospital on the 2nd of March, that a kidney had become available which was a perfect match and the transplant was carried out on the 3rd of March. And so far, progress has been good and the medical staff at the hospital are pleased. My health is improving as each day passes and all made possible by a gift from a very special person.

Thank you, Shirley

It is now 5 years since Shirley had her kidney transplant. The same organ donor gave the 'gift of life' to both Shirley and Susan.

To the family that gave me life

Since my transplant operation two years ago today, I have often sat down to write to you, but on each occasion I have not been able to find the right words. When the first anniversary came round a year ago, I still had difficulty coming to terms with what had happened – and when I tried to express my gratitude to you for the gift of life, the result seemed shallow and trivial in the light of the grief you were no doubt suffering.

I am not a particularly religious person, but I was brought up as a Christian and the Easter story with its combination of joy and sorrow has always been an inspiration. This Easter, I took the unusual step (for me) of going to church on Easter Sunday and came to realise, during the service, that it was incredibly selfish of me never to have written to say thank you. I am doing that now and hope you will forgive me this long delay.

I don't know how much they told you about me but one of the reasons I found it difficult to write to you was that, to a large degree, my liver disease was my own fault, being caused primarily by drink. It seemed grossly unfair to me that I should survive at a time when you were suffering a sad bereavement.

I was not a down-and-out alcoholic – just a busy journalist who had slowly drifted into the habit of drinking too much. My liver eventually

"...I live life to the full in a way I would not have thought possible a few years ago. Every waking moment has taken on a new and special significance..."

failed almost completely (with no prior warning) while I was on a sailing holiday in April 1990. Over the next year I repeatedly fell into deep comas and almost died on several occasions, despite having given up drinking entirely. It was a year of almost unimaginable misery – until that life-saving operation in April 1991.

I now wonder whether you might like to know what I have done with this precious gift. Well, for a start, I live life to the full in a way I would not have thought possible a few years ago. Every waking moment has taken on a new and special significance; I will never again complain about the weather, or say I am bored. I feel I have a duty, as it were, to keep myself as healthy as possible. I do a lot of walking, cycling and sailing and in July, I am taking part in the National Transplant Games, an event designed as a celebration of life. It is a way of proving to the world that joy and optimism can emerge from tragedy. I also feel that I have a debt to repay. I am an active member of the hospital's patient support group and spend a good deal of time helping to raise money for research into diseases such as liver cancer and also trying to help other liver patients. I know from my own experience that talking of their problems and fears can be a great help. I have also bought a computer and learnt all about desktop publishing. I use it to produce a quarterly patients' newsletter which, I'm told, is a source of comfort to many suffering from liver ailments of various kinds.

As you can probably imagine, all this adds up to a style of life which is radically different from that which I led before. I can only hope that, by making myself useful to others, I can in a small way pay the debt I owe you.

There is always the possibility, of course, that we might meet. I do not want to push you one way or the other, beyond saying that I would like to meet the family that has enabled all this to happen – and hear your side of the story.

Finally, I would like to apologise once again for the long delay in writing – and assure you that the gift of life you have bestowed on me is treasured and will not be squandered. My sympathy, love and thanks go to you on this sad anniversary.

Paul

Since his transplant in 1991, Paul has led an active life both professionally and personally. He has married and enjoys family life. Recently, Paul has been battling cancer but remains positive and continues to work.

"...My new life is amazing. I haven't run a marathon or sailed round the world, but being able to go for long walks is, for me, remarkable. Being able to do everyday, ordinary things is a miracle..."

Diana Sanders - transplant recipient

When you died in 2002, my new life began. I want you and your family to know that I will never stop thinking of you, and never stop being grateful for giving me your heart and lungs. Life before my transplant was very different from now. I was born with a congenital heart condition that meant breathing was always a problem. There was nothing that could be done – I was born too soon to benefit from the surgery that babies like me get nowadays. My parents were told I wouldn't survive adolescence – my mother, especially, lived in fear of losing her little girl. I was lucky, though, and lived a good, if limited, life until my 40s, before my heart and lungs started to fail.

My last two years were spent on oxygen, in a wheelchair, my death just round the corner. I couldn't walk across a room or get dressed and needed constant looking after. I knew my

"...being able to walk down the road and post a letter, cycling to work, breathing without thinking about it – sharing a joke with my husband, going to the cinema..."

only hope was a transplant but I don't think it hit me that this would involve someone else's death until I got the call, late that Saturday night in June. I knew then, in all my terror at facing a huge operation, all the worry about not surviving the surgery, that something awful had happened to someone else.

When I came round from the operation, you were my first thought. Who were you? How did you die? I was only told that you were a 31-year-old woman – it seemed like such a terrible age to die, and at times, unfair that I had survived and you hadn't. I hope you never knew anything about the brain haemorrhage that killed you. I hope you were happy and fulfilled, and that your short life was a good one. Did you have children, brothers and sisters, aunts, uncles? What did you enjoy? What made you laugh? I only know that at some stage in your life you made a decision to be an organ donor. Maybe you didn't give it much thought, just saw it as something good to do.

I sometimes think about what might have happened just before the phone call in June 2002. That Saturday night, your life disappearing, your family desperately hoping you would recover, then having to face losing you. Then, your family agreeing that parts of you could be used to help others – an amazing, heroic decision at what must have been an impossibly painful time. I wasn't the only life you saved – your liver, kidneys, pancreas and corneas were given to others as well.

To begin with, my new heart and lungs didn't feel like mine. I mourned the loss of my own heart and lungs, as though they had died, too. I had a strange heartbeat, and I would listen to it and feel as if it belonged somewhere else. Breathing felt really odd – you had huge, healthy lungs and they were so strange compared with my old diseased ones. But over time, they have settled down. Someone told me that they were a gift from you to me, and that helped me to accept them. I hardly think about it now; my body just feels normal and I've got used to being well and alive.

My new life is amazing. I haven't run a marathon or sailed round the world, but being able to go for long walks is, for me, remarkable. Being able to do everyday, ordinary things is a miracle – being able to walk down the road and post a letter, cycling to work, breathing without thinking about it – sharing a joke with my husband, going to the cinema, looking after my mother as she gets older. Looking after other people for a change. Just life, really. My life, in exchange for yours. Thank you.

Diana Sanders

Dear Family

One is never really ready to write a letter like this, but if it had not been for the generosity of your son being a donor, my liver transplant may not have taken place. Myself, a 50 year old mother, naturally feels very sad for you in your loss, but hope you will find some satisfaction in knowing that at present your son's gift has given me a new lease of life and very much happiness to my husband and two sons. I hope that our grateful thanks will give you some comfort during your sadness.

Most sincerely yours

Fourteen years on, this lady remains well and enjoys family life.

Dear Family

Having been a secretary all my life letter writing has always come easy, until now – never did I believe I would be looking for the words to thank the family of the person who, without expecting anything in return, gave our family something so precious.

When my husband George was diagnosed with liver cancer, following a scan at Christmas 2003, I can't begin to explain how we all felt. Then last June, following treatment, the Royal Free doctors told us that the cancer had been shrunk and that a liver transplant was now possible. George was introduced to the transplant coordinators who supported us and explained that there were people who cared and wanted, should anything happen to them, to give others the chance of living.

On the 14th December this year the coordinators contacted us and in the early hours of the next morning, 15th, George had the liver transplant that gave us all new hope.

We have spoken many times about the stranger who we never knew, and who never knew us, who had given us a gift too precious to put a value on – George finds it very emotional as he feels there are no words to explain how grateful he feels and he gets tearful imagining who could care enough to do this for him. This is the reason he has asked me to try to explain our feelings and to write and thank you not just on his behalf, but on behalf of all our family.

One thing we can assure you of is that this special gift will always be treasured and the person who made this possible always remembered.

Our gratitude and thanks always – George, Brenda and Family

It is now 6 years since George's transplant. He is a very humble man and grateful for this incredible gift, which has enabled him to continue to give love and support to his family.

> "...ONE THING WE CAN ASSURE YOU OF IS THAT THIS SPECIAL GIFT WILL ALWAYS BE TREASURED AND THE PERSON WHO MADE THIS POSSIBLE ALWAYS REMEMBERED..."

I have wanted to write to you for some time but have only recently become well enough to do so.

My most grateful thanks go to you both for your thoughtfulness towards others, at a time when you were suffering a great personal tragedy.

Due to your kindness, I received your daughter's liver and your action undoubtedly saved my life.

I was suddenly struck by a mystery virus that rapidly and completely destroyed my liver and had a new one not been found within a day or two, I would have died.

As a parent myself, I know that this must be the darkest part of your lives, however, I hope it will be of some comfort to know that through her death, your daughter has saved another's life.

Once again, I thank you both so very much.

Patricia

Patricia received her transplant eight years ago, after she suffered acute liver failure. She made a good recovery and, with her renewed health, enjoys travelling and being with her family.

Dear Friend or Friends

My birth name is Kay and I am the fortunate recipient of Rita's liver.

A beautiful Acer Palmatum has been planted in the Temple garden in Amaravati Buddhist Monastery in Great Gaddesden, Hertfordshire, which is located just outside Hemel Hempstead. This enables Rita's memory to be honoured every day. Luang Por Sumedho, Senior Monk at the monastery has kindly offered to bless it; also he is a very highly revered Buddhist teacher.

If you are ever in the area and able to get to the monastery, to see the bush, you would be most welcome to visit. Please go to the main office and ask for the gardener who could show you the Acer bush planted by Rocana [my Buddhist name], the present gardener has kindly offered to show you where the bush is. If no one is available the bush is located to the right of the temple in from the wheelchair entrance, where it looks very beautiful. If I can get my son to take a photograph I will send it to you, but it would be truly wonderful if you could see it yourself.

Dana [a meal offering] has been given several times to the monastery's community, in Rita's memory, and that of her husband. I am sorry that I do not know your father's name, but they are always revered together.

Rita's great gift is looking after me very well, I have been told that I have gone from looking like a "little grey ghost", I am now beginning to be able to do things not just sit and be. I will always give many thanks for the great gift that was donated to me, by a very beautiful human being.

With much Metta [loving kindness] and in peace.

My gratitude always

Kay had her liver transplant 14 years ago and continues to give thanks for her wonderful gift.

"...my new liver has made an incredible difference to my life. I can now lead a normal life and have returned to work. I have also taken part in the Transplant Games..."

Dear Friend

Now that time has passed since my liver transplant, I would like to take this opportunity of writing to you in order that I can somehow express my gratitude to you for my second chance of life. I deliberately delayed writing to you earlier as I realise that the past must have been very difficult for you, although you have often been in my thoughts.

I thought it would be nice for you to know about me. I am 48 years old, married and have two children; a son of 18 and a daughter of 21 so plenty of hormones! I have worked full time at the Open University Business School for the past nine years and I have just finished my BSc Hons. Up to July 2000 I lived life to the full. However, after that date I suffered an acute liver disease that would eventually be life threatening, a liver transplant being my only hope.

Apparently the liver is often referred to as the "silent" organ, often forgotten and not talked about. Indeed it was only when my liver was not functioning properly that I could comprehend how ill I had felt and how the quality of my life had severely declined, sleeping most of the time with the simplest of tasks becoming difficult. However, since my liver transplant on the 17th October my new liver has made an incredible difference to my life. I can now lead a normal life and have returned to work. I have also taken part in the Transplant Games for the last two years.

Spending so many months in hospital gave me plenty of time to reflect on what was happening to me. I felt so lucky to be given the chance of a liver transplant; as there are many patients with liver diseases that are either too sick to undergo the surgery or where a transplant is just not possible. Also, there are plenty of people who reside in other societies who do not have the same NHS facilities as we do here in the UK, eg the third world countries and transplantation would not even be a considered option, so I have been very fortunate.

I have planted a shrub in our garden in remembrance and to show my appreciation to your loved one of my gift.

If in the future you would either like to meet or write to me I would very much welcome this. However, if you would rather not I would understand.

With my very best sincere wishes, Pamela

Pamela has made the most of the past 10 years following her liver transplant, studying and being promoted in her work every few years, as well as appreciating her family and friends.

Dear Jim, Mark and Wayne

Thank you very much for my Christmas card and letter, which I received on the 18th January.

I am still keeping well, happy and lucky to be alive, thanks to you all.

My daughter, Maria, is indeed very fortunate to have a healthy mummy now looking after her.

Together every night we have a prayer for everyone who has helped her mummy to stay alive.

Best wishes to you all and GOD BLESS.

Nora, Ronald and Maria (January 1999)

Dear Jim, Mark and Wayne

Thank you for your Christmas card. My Christmas is not completely happy until I receive your card.

It is another gift that you give me and that I seem to expect now every year. I cannot thank you enough for your kind generosity.

I had a good, healthy year, full of life and wanting to do so much…

Maria is now 12 years old. She has started her senior school and is doing pretty well. She is growing into a kind, friendly young lady.

I feel privileged to be able to tuck her in bed every night.

Thank you for giving me the chance to do it.

God bless.

Nora, Roland and Maria (January 2002)

Dear Jim, Mark and Wayne

Thank you for your Christmas card. Did you enjoy your trip to Thailand? I am still doing pretty well and every day is a new gift, full of challenges thanks to you.

Maria is 14 years old now, going on 18! She is full of life and a joy to watch growing.

I hope your family and yourself are keeping well. You are always in my thoughts; especially on this day.

Thank you for my new life.

Best wishes.

Nora (December 2003)

Nora remains well 13 years after her liver transplant and appreciates even the simple aspects of family life. She continues to be in regular contact with Jim, Mark and Wayne.

> *"…I am still doing pretty well and every day is a new gift, full of challenges thanks to you…"*

Dear Friend

This letter is to thank you for the gift of my life. As you can imagine this letter is very hard to write, only because of the sadness you have had to endure. But if it is of any consolation the liver transplant operation was very successful, I am in good health.

Maybe you would like to know a bit about me, I was born in Italy and came to London when I was twenty one, I am now fifty five years old, unmarried, but have two nephews and three nieces, these children lost their fathers through cancer at a young age, so I do know a bit about the sadness you are going through, as they were my brothers.

My transplant was on the 12th of December, it was a bit shock to get the phone call to go to the hospital, but the staff there were excellence itself and because of you, and them, I am alive today.

Also I would like to add that people around me now know how important it is to donate organs, it has shown them that life can be given to really sick people as I was. Once again thank you so much.

God bless, Alberto

Alberto had his liver transplant 11 years ago. He is a very humble man who has worked hard all his life to support his family.

Dear Friends

This is a strange and hard letter for me to write, but I feel compelled to write to you to let you know who I am and what you have done for me. About 7 months ago now, I was given the most amazing gift, a chance to live, and I have you and your family to thank for this.

Over a year ago I started getting extremely ill and after going through a long process to try and discover exactly what the problem was, the doctors concluded that my liver was damaged beyond repair due to a genetic disease and I would need to have a transplant. The amount of donors is limited and so I was put on the waiting list until a suitable match was found. The donor finally came and I was blessed to be given the organ from your beloved one. The operation was a complete success and I made a speedy recovery (the doctors were even impressed with my fast progress).

Now, 7 months on, I am living a normal healthy life, and as a young man, I hope to be able to live for a long time to come. I really cannot begin to express how indebted I feel towards your loved one, and your entire family, for giving me the chance to live. I realise that this period must have been extremely difficult for you, but I hope that it brings you comfort to know that your generosity has saved my life. I will always be grateful to you for donating an organ and allowing me the gift of life.

With all my love and thanks

Six years on, this young man is 27 years old and enjoying a very healthy life.

"...The operation was a complete success and I made a speedy recovery (the doctors were even impressed with my fast progress)..."

"...I would love the donor family to know that their brave decision not only saved my life, but it transformed all our lives. We've been able to move on from illness and benefits..."

Steve Peak - transplant recipient

"...thank you from the bottom of my heart for giving me this chance of a future with my wife and children. It takes a very special kind of person to do what you have done..."

Dear Friend

My name is Steve. I am 37 years old and I am married to Becky. We have children aged 10, 9, 6 and 11 months old.

About 5½ years ago I was diagnosed with liver disease; after many tests the doctors could not find a cause for what I had.

In April 2003 I became very ill and ended up in ITU on life support for 4 weeks; due to this I was told by the doctors that I would need a transplant.

After just 4 weeks on the list I got a phone call to tell me I needed to come to hospital for the operation. I had a successful transplant in September and spent just 3 weeks in hospital. I am now on the road to recovery and looking forward to a much healthier future with my family.

I would like to thank you from the bottom of my heart for giving me this chance of a future with my wife and children. It takes a very special kind of person to do what you have done. At Christmas we had a special candle alight for your family member who gave me this new life.

We would like to offer our deepest sympathy to all of you in your loss and again thank you so much for our chance of a happy future.

All our love and thanks to you from Steve, Becky, and all his family

Since Steve's transplant seven years ago, he has managed to find work and is employed in his local hospital as a porter. He feels he can now be the father and husband he always wanted to be.

Dear Friends

I am writing to offer my sincere condolences to all of your family on the tragic loss of your loved one and to thank you with all my heart on the brave decision you made at such a sad time in allowing their organs to be used for transplantation. I am a woman of 46 years with 2 children and 5 grandchildren. I was diagnosed with a liver disease [primary biliary cirrhosis] in 1991, but was told that I probably had this since my twenties. I have certainly been ill since then and gradually went downhill. It is a progressive disease and very debilitating with numerous symptoms, resulting in my having no quality of life whatsoever.

My days consisted in my having to stay in bed nearly all day, not able to do anything and feeling very depressed at feeling so tired and constantly in pain. I was told the only option was a liver transplant as I only had about 2 years to live.

I had mixed feelings trying to come to terms with this, frightened at having to go through with the transplant wondering if I would survive it, and also knowing that someone had lost their life leaving their loved ones behind.

I cannot express how grateful I am for your courage in allowing me another chance of life and giving me back to my family.

I will cherish the gift you have given to me, and will treat my new liver with the utmost respect it deserves, it is part of me now, and I will never forget my donor, or my donor's family for saving my life.

God bless you all at this most difficult time and always I remain a very grateful recipient.

This, and the two following letters demonstrate the effect a wonderful gift can have on a family.

Dear Donor Family

Please accept my deepest sympathy on the tragic loss of your loved one. I can only guess at the courage it takes at a time of such great sadness to make the decision that you made to allow your loved one to become an organ donor.

I find it hard to find the appropriate words to convey to you how truly grateful I am that you showed such courage.

In 1981 my wife was diagnosed as suffering from PBC. This is a disease in which her immune system attacked her liver. This caused her many problems, such as chronic pain, chronic fatigue, arthritis, eye problems and worst of all constant terrible itching, which prevented her from sleeping. As the years went on all the symptoms became far worse until she reached a point where she felt that she had no quality of life. At this stage she developed severe depression.

"...I will cherish the gift you have given to me, and will treat my new liver with the utmost respect it deserves, it is part of me now, and I will never forget my donor, or my donor's family for saving my life..."

The deterioration in her condition continued and she was told that without a transplant she only had two years to live.

Your decision not only saved her life, but will enable her to have a far greater quality of life after many years of terrible suffering.

I will never forget the debt that I owe you and your family. We are not deeply religious people, but we do believe in God and we often visit churches and cathedrals. On these visits we always light two candles in memory of relations that have now departed, on future visits we shall light an extra candle in memory of the donor who has made it possible for my wife to have a far better quality of life. I will be eternally grateful to you and your family and I will never forget the debt that I owe to you.

**Many, many thanks –
Yours, a very grateful husband**

Dear Donor Family
Please accept our sincere condolences on the tragic loss of your loved one.

We would like you to know that by making the decision to donate your loved one's liver, you have given our mum a chance not only to live, but in time to lead a pain free life. We thank you wholeheartedly for that.

As a family we are truly sorry for your loss as we can only imagine the pain and grief that you have suffered and continue to come to terms with.

The decision to donate must have been very difficult, but by doing this you have given a 46 year old woman life, as she was given 2 years to live. This would not have been quality living as mum was very ill, mainly bed ridden and in constant pain.

The donor and her family will always be in our thoughts and prayers

God bless, the recipient's daughters

Diary Extract Oct 2008
How blessed I feel one year on from my operation. How close I feel to my donor family. I am celebrating a truly wonderful year with my daughter, son, grandson, partner and friends, but I am close to them, the family whose compassion has given me my life back. Who was she? A daughter, a wife, a mother, a sister, a friend, I will never know.

I will always live my life through her compassion to donate and will live it well with joy, happiness, understanding and love.

Theresa

A whole year on:
A year to be a grandma
A year to be a mother
A year to be a wife
A year to be a sister
A year to be a friend
A year to travel
A year to paint
A year to garden
A year to thank God for this
A year for reflection
A year to feel close to my donor family
as they move through their grief
A year of deep, deep joy and a year
I did not expect to achieve

I wanted to let you know that thanks to your daughter I have had this past year as a gift.

It has been a year of mixed emotions mostly filled with joy and happiness, but sad when I think of the sacrifice that you and your family have made. I am so grateful for the opportunity to live again.

My husband and my son and I thank you deeply.

——

The following letters were written by the recipient and family members in the period soon after her transplant, and highlight the positive impact of donation on the family unit.

To the donor
Thank you for helping my mummy get better and she is feeling very well.

Yours sincerely, Harry

Dear Family
Yesterday, I was at the home of my daughter-in-law who had a liver transplant last Saturday, when the telephone rang, I picked it up to be told that someone wanted to speak to my grandson. I passed it over to him saying that there was a call for him.

"Is it daddy?" he asked.
"No" I said.

The expression on his face as he shouted "Mummy" will stay with us all our lives. From the bottom of our hearts, my wife and I thank you for forethought and your concurrence in donating the liver. We thought of you then and promise that whenever we see that wonderful happy expression on our grandson's face – we will also think of you.

Our daughter-in-law is a lovely person. Thank you for giving back her life and for saving a little boy from the heartache of losing his mummy.

Dear Family
I want you to know that for the first time in several years of suffering I feel well. I am a mother of a child who has just turned seven years old, for my part I am 34 years old. I want to thank you from the bottom of my heart for your precious gift by giving your agreement to offer me the liver of your daughter; you have allowed me to relive with hope in happiness, in joy and with serenity and with a renewed strength. I have just returned home and on arriving at the front door my greatest happiness was to see my child run into my arms – you will understand. I cannot describe to you the "joy of life", that a child gives in his smile which is like a day of sunshine.

My wait was long and hard to tolerate, when the hospital called us exactly two weeks ago. My blood froze in my body, my heart beat a hundred miles and I was full of different emotions. I felt frightened, sad, but also an intense joy. The night in the hospital before the operation was the most difficult emotionally. I had decided to put myself on autopilot waiting for the operation.

On Saturday morning I was beside myself with fear. The operation was uncomplicated taking 5½ hours, which was very short comparatively.

After leaving the operating theatre I had to battle for life in intensive care.

"...I want to thank you deeply for the hard decision you took to give me the force to live..."

> *"...I sincerely hope it can be of some consolation to you and your family that your "gift" has enabled me to continue to lead a normal life..."*

The Sunday evening I was moved to the liver ward for the "long recovery". Until Wednesday I had not really taken in the enormity of what had happened (being in so much pain), but by the evening a fantastic realisation dawned on me with assistance from the nurses. I managed to get out of bed having a force in me that I was slowly discovering, a force to fight, to be strong and well again.

This strength came from your daughter. I felt my new liver give me hope and told me to fight and all will be well again. I want to thank you deeply for the hard decision you took to give me the force to live. I know that you must be going through an impossible time, but please understand that a part of your daughter has given me a second birth, which is unbelievably fabulous.

Once again my husband, my son and me thank you for your delicate decision with our heart. If you feel the need to contact me please do not hesitate to contact me through the coordinators. It would be a pleasure for me to respond to you.

Sincerely best wishes

It is now 8 years since Sophie's transplant and she has been able to see her son grow up and be a mother with all the energy needed for the role.

Dear Sir
Thank you for giving me the opportunity of writing to you again. I am sorry I have taken so long to do so.

Since I wrote to you last October I am pleased to say my health has continued to improve and I now feel I am getting back to my former self. At the moment I am waiting for a call from the hospital to go in for my yearly "MOT", albeit overdue. Still I feel confident that all will be well. As I mentioned in my last letter we are making arrangements for a tree to be dedicated at Wimpole Park, Cambridgeshire, in memory and gratitude. This will be in September.

Hopefully, time has eased the pain of your loss and I sincerely hope it can be of some consolation to you and your family that your "gift" has enabled me to continue to lead a normal life. That "gift" can only be the greatest one anyone can receive and I reiterate mine and my family's thanks to you.

Ideally, I would like to be able to thank you in person, but obviously I appreciate this would have to be acceptable to you and I would understand if you preferred not to. However, should you agree arrangements can be made through the liver coordinators who can set things in motion.

Thanks, Trevor

Trevor was well for four years following this letter. He then developed chronic rejection and shortly after was re-transplanted. Trevor and his wife had another child following his second transplant and he remains fit and well 20 years after his first transplant.

Dear Friends

There are many special people in life that help and care for others through their lives. These are truly very special people indeed, but people who not only do this, but unselfishly think about helping others if their own life is taken away by donating vital organs to give someone a new life, these are beyond special, they are truly remarkable heroes. Your daughter was indeed a hero.

My wife and I are incredibly touched by the generosity of your family at such a terribly sad time.

Although we did not know her we have cried so many times thinking of your grief, such emotional times for everyone. Our thoughts will always be with you, words cannot express how we feel.

I would like to tell you a little about myself.

I am 44 years old and last Christmas was taken ill and diagnosed with a genetic liver disease. After extensive tests I was privileged to be allowed to go on the liver donor transplant list.

On the early hours of Monday morning the 22nd July I received a call asking me to come to the hospital in London without delay for my operation.

I must confess immediately after the operation was an emotional experience and there were times when I did not think I would make it. I was consumed by thoughts of the courage of the person who unselfishly donated the liver and how lucky I was to receive it. I even had visions of the person speaking to me during recovery telling me it was alright.

During this time I cried tears of great sadness.

I am now recovering with rapid pace and my life can go on, but I will always think of the special person who gave me the gift of life and the special family that allowed it to happen

Michael and Marilyn

"...I WILL ALWAYS THINK OF THE SPECIAL PERSON WHO GAVE ME THE GIFT OF LIFE..."

THAN

To Family of

I'am writing t
kidney you

you have mad
ave one. happy child

he is getting
has all his

Thank you for
better one.

WERE all hap
trans-plant.
WEll.

Fro

.P.S.Thank yo
life a' bette

THANK

Words can't express how thankful we all are for this great gift you have given us all. You have given our son a new life and a future. He had a bit of a rocky start after the operation but all is well now. He says he can enjoy his food now, whereas before he didn't eat much and he says he feels good and he is gaining weight. His body has responded well to the new kidney.

I hope that in some way you find a little comfort by knowing you have given a new life to a child. Thank you – forever in our hearts and thoughts.

Annette and Mark and family

——

I would like to say thank you for what you have done for my Grandson. You have given him a new life and hope for the future. I hope this little note will bring you and yours some comfort at what must be a very sad time.

How can I thank you for such a wonderful gift – only by telling you that my Grandson is now running around and getting into mischief and all because of what you have helped with. God bless and thank you.

From John's grandparent

THANK–YOU
To family of the donor.

I am writing to you about his kidney you have given him.

You have made my brother happy to have one. Happy child and family.

He is getting better and he has all his tubes taken out.

Thank you for making his life a better one.

We're all happy he has had his transplant. He is happy as well.

From his sister (Sarah)

PS Thank you for making his life a better one.

THANK YOU

——

Thanks for the kidney. I am now better than I was.

John

John was 14 years old when he received his kidney transplant. Eight years on, he is well and he and his family remain grateful for his gift.

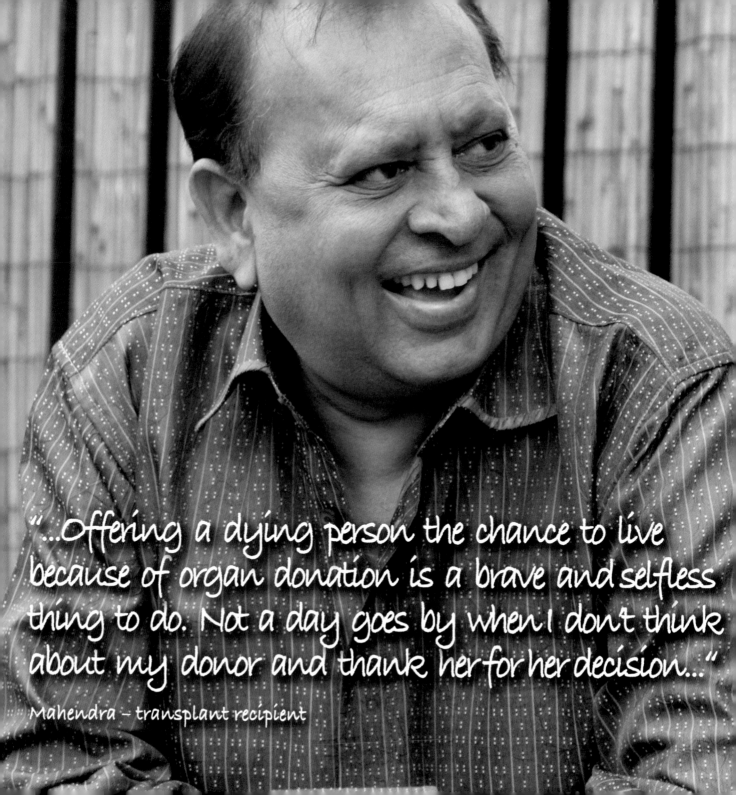

"...Offering a dying person the chance to live because of organ donation is a brave and selfless thing to do. Not a day goes by when I don't think about my donor and thank her for her decision..."

Mahendra – transplant recipient

"...I have started caring for my health, so that I can give all my healthy organs to anybody in need after my death..."

The path of donating organs will not only save a person's life, it will also give it a meaning. The whisper of a donated organ can be heard always – truly. This is a road to liberation. Like an angel 6 years ago came and gave life to my husband by donating her liver – filled my life with joy. I promise, if you pursue this good deed, it will definitely purify the way, to see the world.

Your vision, your thoughts, everything is uplifted. It is beyond all delight, in this experience the donor may not be able to feel – but for the receiver it is truly a great blessing. It uplifts not only you, but your entire world. You can cultivate anything you want in this body – you can let it go to waste, or you can use it as a vehicle that will carry you to the God.

This donation opens a new dimension in our awareness – allowing to dive deeper and deeper inside, and enabling us to touch the source of love in the heart. This full wisdom and power only enables us to make the decision to give our organs – after signing the donor form for the first time in my life, I felt free, uplifted. That very moment I felt more myself than ever before. I have started caring for my health, so that I can give all my healthy organs to anybody in need after my death. I have even convinced many people to fill in the form before it is too late. They do realise and fill it in after seeing my husband's health and the effort of great doctors, nurses, transplant coordinators and all staff. I just can't repay this to the family, who helped that angel's wish come true. May their life be filled with all happiness.

Thank you – everyone

"...knowing that we donated gave us some kind of peace. It was a human decision, and brought some positivity out of this tragedy..."

Bobby Mudhar – brother of Mandip

Bobby and family at Mandip's tournament

Mandip Mudhar's story

Following his untimely passing, Mandip Mudhar's family made the decision to honour their son's wishes and donate some of his organs. Every year his family arrange a football tournament in Mandip's memory to raise awareness of organ donation.

His brother Bobby said: "We've never regretted the decision to donate my brother's organs. He'd said to my sister before that it's what he wanted. Knowing that we donated gave us some kind of peace, It was a human decision, and brought some positivity out of this tragedy."

"Whilst the decision to donate organs is not common place within our culture, our Sikh faith teaches us to serve and help others where we can. Our family took immense comfort in knowing someone else was helped as a result of our donation. If my brother's life could have been saved by receiving an organ then we would of requested help ourselves."

"My brother really enjoyed football and it felt natural that this is how we should remember him and the gift he gave others in passing. The first memorial match was just between my friends and those of my brother. Now we have a tournament every year with up to 40 teams playing from all over the country."

Bobby Mudhar pictured with his daughter

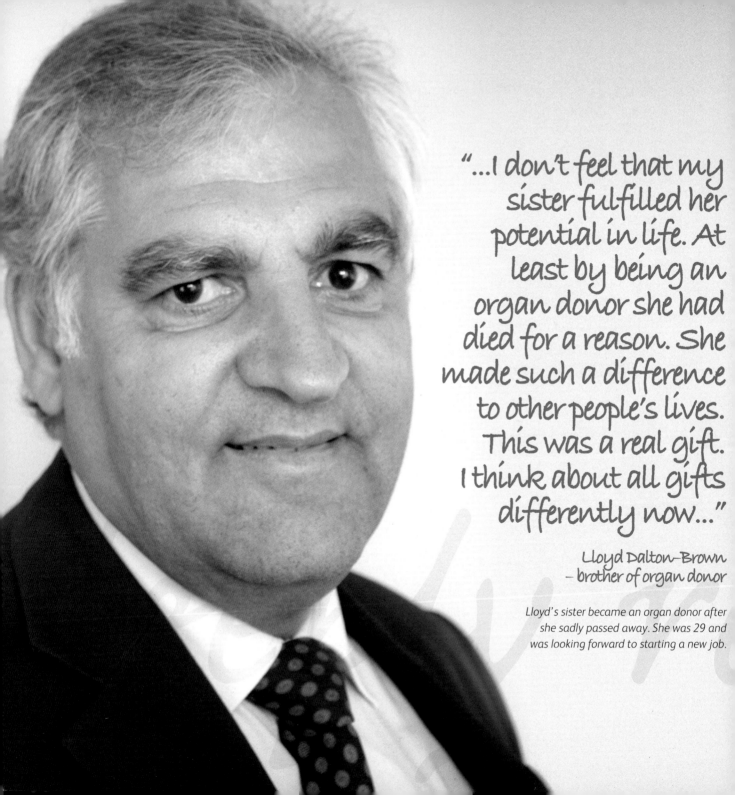

"...I don't feel that my sister fulfilled her potential in life. At least by being an organ donor she had died for a reason. She made such a difference to other people's lives. This was a real gift. I think about all gifts differently now..."

Lloyd Dalton-Brown
– brother of organ donor

Lloyd's sister became an organ donor after she sadly passed away. She was 29 and was looking forward to starting a new job.

If you have been inspired by the stories in this book and would like further information on organ donation and how to register as a donor, the following resources can offer insight, help and advice. By registering as a donor, you will join the many millions of people who have pledged to help others after death by donating life-saving organs. Please remember to tell loved ones about your decision.

To register as a donor
The NHS Organ Donor Register, managed by NHS Blood and Transplant, is the national, confidential list of people who are willing to become donors. Putting your name on the Register makes everyone aware of your wishes and ensures there is a chance that your organs can help someone else – maybe several people – to live after your death. You can join by filling in a form online.

www.organdonation.nhs.uk

Alternatively, you can call the NHS Donor Line on 0300 123 23 23 (Open 24 hours a day, all year round. Calls are charged at your contracted rate for local calls.)

The Donor Family Network
The Donor Family Network is run by donor families for donor families. The Network has two main aims: the support of donor families and the promotion of organ and tissue donation. The symbol of the Donor Family Network comprises a butterfly and a forget-me-not. The butterfly as a symbol of hope and new life and the forget-me-not as no donor will ever be forgotten.

www.donorfamilynetwork.co.uk

Live Life Then Give Life
The charity aims to save and improve the lives of all those in need or receipt of organ and tissue transplants. It exists to improve education and awareness of organ donation and to fund projects that increase the numbers of successful transplants in the UK.

www.lltgl.org.uk

Transplant Support Network
The Transplant Support Network is a nationwide network of volunteer transplant patients and their carers, who provide locally based support for others coping with transplantation. Short or long term support from outside the family has been found to play an invaluable part in the waiting, adjustment and recovery processes.

www.transplantsupportnetwork.org.uk

Freephone support lines
0800 027 4490 or 0800 027 4491

Acknowledgements

This book would not have been possible without the support of many individuals and organisations. In particular, we would like to thank all the donors and their families, the transplant recipients and their families who wrote the letters included in this book and participants in the donor recognition workshop, September 2009. We are also grateful to all those patients who were supportive of this book from the beginning and gave consent for their letters to be published but these may not have been included at the end.

We would also like to thank the following:

Department of Health

Anne Milton, parliamentary under secretary of state for public health; Chris Rudge, national clinical director for transplantation; and their colleagues within the Department of Health.

NHS Blood and Transplant

Sally Johnson, director of organ donation and transplantation; Gavin Evans, assistant director with responsibility for the organ donation campaign; and the donor and recipient coordinators throughout the UK for their help in contacting families and transplant recipients.

Royal College of Physicians

Sir Ian Gilmore, past president; Sir Richard Thompson, president; Martin Else, chief executive; James Partridge, designer; and Suzanne Fuzzey, production controller and RCP project manager.

Royal Free Hospital

The Liver Transplant Team; Barbara Chandler, PA to Professor Burroughs, for her work transcribing the letters.

Cover

Gift of Life, oil on canvas, by Helen Eccles – a transcription of Duccio's *Annunciation*.

Photography and additional text

Jennie Jewitt-Harris and Victoria Lush

(DH) Department
of Health

NHS
Blood and Transplant